Superphonics

The simplest, fastest way to teach your child to read

Contents

a division of Hodder Headline

Introduction

What is meant by the term 'phonics'?

Phonics is a highly effective way of teaching reading and spelling, based on the link between sounds and the way in which we write them down. A unit of sound is called a phoneme (*foe-neem*), and the written version of it is called a grapheme:

c / a / t contains 3 graphemes and 3 phonemes

ch / a / t contains 3 graphemes and 3 phonemes

f / l / a / t contains 4 graphemes and 4 phonemes

Note: A phoneme may contain more than one letter. A letter has a name: ***dee***
and a sound: ***d*** *(d)*

Letters are divided into 2 groups:
Vowels: ***a e i o u***
Consonants: ***b c d f g h j k l m n p q r s t v w x y z***

How does *Superphonics* teach this?

There are 5 books in the series. The chart on the inside front cover shows which graphemes/ phonemes are taught in each book. Each book builds on the skills already learned, and there are plenty of opportunities for revision and practice.

Each book is divided into units, all of which are organised in the same way.

Each unit in this book consists of 3 steps:

STEP 1 HEAR THE SOUND
Your child is encouraged to listen hard for the first letter sound in a word, and to think of more words beginning with that sound.

STEP 2 READ THE LETTER
Now your child is taught how to recognise the printed version of the letter with the help of a 'letter-picture'.

STEP 3 WRITE THE LETTER
Again referring to the letter-picture, your child learns how to write the letter.

Each unit in Books 2–5 consists of 6 steps:

STEP 1 FIND THE RHYMING WORDS
The ability to rhyme is an important skill. If your child can read and spell ***cat***, he or she will be able to read and spell ***mat*** – and so on.

STEP 2 FIND THE SOUNDS
Now your child is taught to hear the separate phonemes in a word: ***c / a / t***. Most children need to be taught that each word is made up of individual sounds. This comes in Book 3.

STEP 3 BLEND THE SOUNDS
The little alien Phoneme Fred is useful here. Poor Phoneme Fred can only speak in separate phonemes – ***c / a / t*** – and your child will be able to help him to blend these into a spoken word.

STEP 4 SPLIT THE WORD INTO SOUNDS
Hearing the phonemes, and saying them in quick succession, prepares children for spelling.

STEP 5 READ THE WORD
Your child is taught how to read the word phoneme by phoneme, always going from left to right.

STEP 6 SPELL THE WORD
This is a writing activity, in which your child will learn how to turn the phonemes into graphemes, or written letters. Ask your child to read his or her writing back to you.

Some children take time to learn how to write. Don't spend too long on this step, and don't worry if your child's spelling is not developing as quickly as his or her reading.

This is a unit from Book 1.

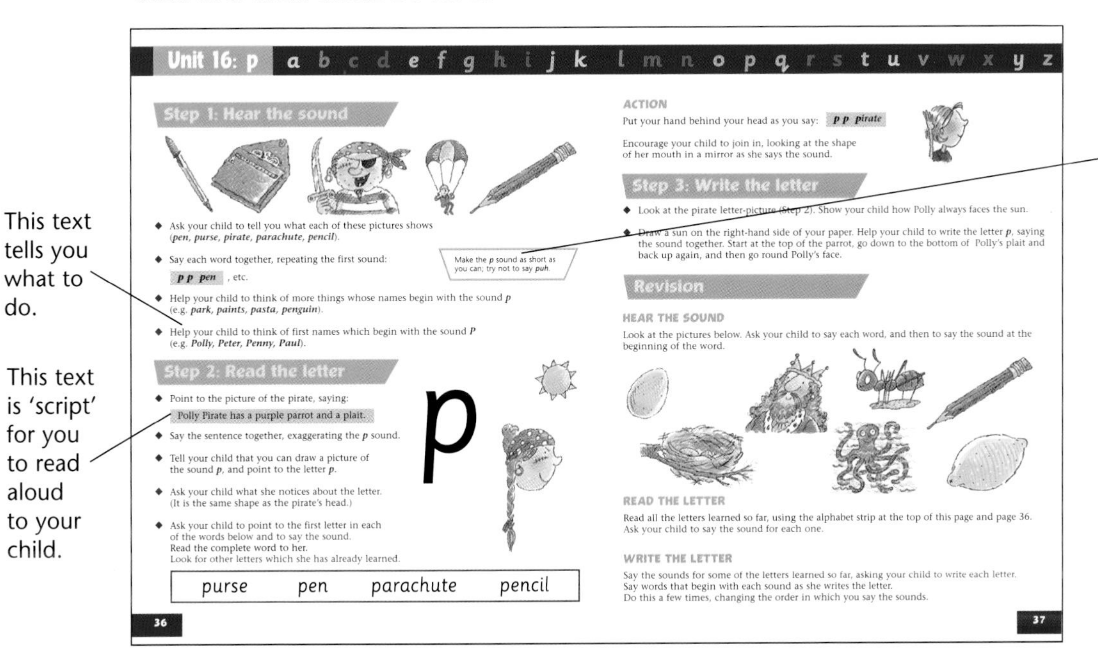

Unit 16: p a b c d e f g h i j k l m n o p q r s t u v w x y z

Step 1: Hear the sound

- Ask your child to tell you what each of these pictures shows (***pen, purse, pirate, parachute, pencil***).
- Say each word together, repeating the first sound: ***p p pen*** , etc.
- Help your child to think of more things whose names begin with the sound ***p*** (e.g. ***park, paints, pasta, penguin***).
- Help your child to think of first names which begin with the sound ***P*** (e.g. ***Polly, Peter, Penny, Paul***).

Make the ***p*** sound as short as you can; try not to say ***puh***.

Step 2: Read the letter

- Point to the picture of the pirate, saying: Polly Pirate has a purple parrot and a plait.
- Say the sentence together, exaggerating the ***p*** sound.
- Tell your child that you can draw a picture of the sound ***p***, and point to the letter ***p***.
- Ask your child what she notices about the letter. (It is the same shape as the pirate's head.)
- Ask your child to point to the first letter in each of the words below and to say the sound. Read the complete word to her. Look for other letters which she has already learned.

p

purse pen parachute pencil

36

ACTION

Put your hand behind your head as you say: ***p p pirate***

Encourage your child to join in, looking at the shape of her mouth in a mirror as she says the sound.

Step 3: Write the letter

- Look at the pirate letter-picture (Step 2). Show your child how Polly always faces the sun.
- Draw a sun on the right-hand side of your paper. Help your child to write the letter ***p***, saying the sound together. Start at the top of the parrot, go down to the bottom of Polly's plait and back up again, and then go round Polly's face.

Revision

HEAR THE SOUND

Look at the pictures below. Ask your child to say each word, and then to say the sound at the beginning of the word.

READ THE LETTER

Read all the letters learned so far, using the alphabet strip at the top of this page and page 36. Ask your child to say the sound for each one.

WRITE THE LETTER

Say the sounds for some of the letters learned so far, asking your child to write each letter. Say words that begin with each sound as she writes the letter. Do this a few times, changing the order in which you say the sounds.

37

This text tells you what to do.

This text is 'script' for you to read aloud to your child.

Helpful hints are printed in boxes like this.

How do I know it will work?

In the author's school, where this method is used, the reading ages of children in Years 2 to 4 are about 2 years higher than their actual ages.

I'm not a teacher – will I be able to do it?

Yes! ***Superphonics*** is clearly structured and clearly written, in plain English. The 'step' method of working will rapidly become familiar to you and your child.

My life is very busy – how much time will it take up?

If you spend just 20 minutes on ***Superphonics*** each day, your child will make swift progress. Book 1 will take about 4 weeks, Book 2 will take 2-6 weeks and Books 3-5 will each take 1-2 weeks to complete. If you can't manage 20 minutes every day, don't worry. Just do what you can.

Will I need to collect lots of bits and pieces before we can start?

No! All you need, apart from the books, is a notebook or a few sheets of paper, and a sharp pencil. A small mirror (for looking at mouth shape) is useful but not essential.

Will *Superphonics* enable my child to read stories?

Yes! He or she will be able to read stories, street signs, lists, adverts – and lots more! But don't wait until you have finished ***Superphonics*** to share books and other kinds of reading.

This book teaches the alphabet, and the sound each letter makes when it comes at the beginning of a word. 'Letter-pictures', such as the dinosaur shaped like a ***d***, will help your child to recognise the letters. Each letter-picture has a picture of the sun on its right. In the dinosaur example, the dinosaur is looking at the sun, i.e. from left to right. This will help your child to understand that we always start writing on the left-hand side of the page, and move towards the right.

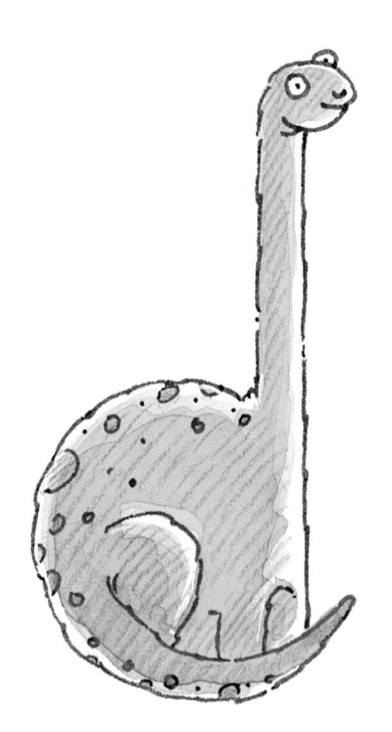

All the letter-pictures are shown on the opposite page, and alphabet tiles are provided at the back of the book.

ch, ***sh*** and ***th*** are taught at the end of the book, because each of these is a single phoneme and occurs at the beginning of many words in English. At this stage, it is best to refer to a letter by its sound (***d***) rather than its name (***dee***). In this way, your child will not become confused at this vital first stage.

b
c
d
e
g
h
i
j
l
m
n
o
q
r
s
t
v
w
x
y
ch
sh
th

Step 1: Hear the sound

- Ask your child to tell you what each of these pictures shows (***apple, acrobat, ankle, ant, astronaut***).
- Say each word together, repeating the first sound:

  a a apple, etc.

> Make sure all the words and names begin with the short ***a*** sound; for example, ***ape*** and ***Aaron*** begin with long ***a*** sounds.

- Help your child to think of more things whose names begin with the sound ***a*** (e.g. ***axe, alligator, ambulance, animal***).
- Help your child to think of first names which begin with the sound ***a*** (e.g. ***Andy, Anna, Andrew, Abigail***).

Step 2: Read the letter

- Point to the picture of the apple, saying:

  Annie and Afshana eat apples.

- Say the sentence together, exaggerating the ***a*** sound.
- Tell your child that you can draw a picture of the sound ***a***, and point to the letter ***a***.
- Ask your child what he notices about the letter. (It is the same shape as the apple.)
- Ask your child to point to the first letter in each of the words below, and to say the sound. Read the complete word to him. Look for another letter ***a*** in the word ***acrobat***.

> Help your child to understand that a sound can be represented by a written symbol.

> The letter-picture of the apple will help your child to remember the shape of the letter ***a***.

apple	ant	ankle	acrobat

ACTION

Pretend to be holding a large apple in your hand. Take a huge bite out of the apple, opening your mouth as wide as you can as you say:

a a apple

Encourage your child to join in, looking at the shape of his mouth in a mirror as he says the sound.

Use the actions when you revise the letters each day.

Step 3: Write the letter

- Look at the apple letter-picture (Step 2). Point out the fact that the side with the stalk is nearer to the sun.

- Draw a sun on the right-hand side of your page or sheet of paper. Help your child to write the letter ***a***, saying the sound together. Start at the top right-hand side, curl around the apple (away from the sun), go back up to the starting point and then draw the curly stalk.

This will help your child to understand that we write from left to right.

Thinking about the apple will help your child to remember the letter shape.

Don't worry if your child finds it difficult to form the letter.

Step 1: Hear the sound

- Ask your child to tell you what each of these pictures shows (***ball, bat, boot, bicycle, bag***).
- Say each word together, repeating the first sound:

  b b ball, etc.

Make the ***b*** sound as short as you can; try not to say ***buh***.

- Help your child to think of more things whose names begin with the sound ***b*** (e.g. ***banana, baby, bear, biscuit***).
- Help your child to think of first names which begin with the sound ***b*** (e.g. ***Bethany, Beatrice, Bruno, Barry***).

Step 2: Read the letter

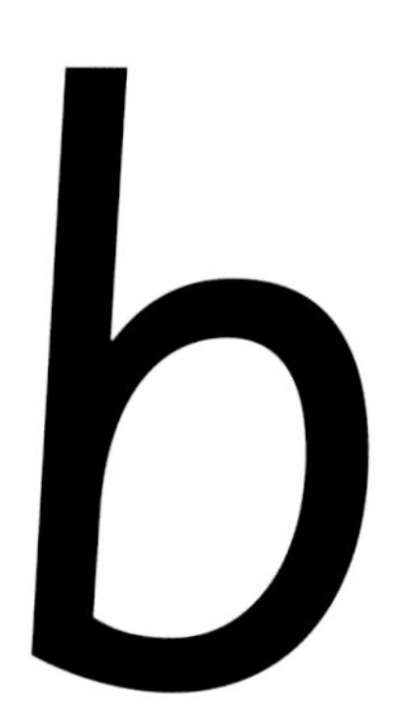

- Point to the picture of the boot, saying:

  This is Bonnie's big brown boot.

- Say the sentence together, exaggerating the ***b*** sound.
- Tell your child that you can draw a picture of the sound ***b***, and point to the letter ***b***.
- Ask your child what she notices about the letter. (It is the same shape as the boot.)
- Ask your child to point to the first letter in each of the words below and to say the sound. Read the complete word to her. Look for the letter ***a*** in the words.

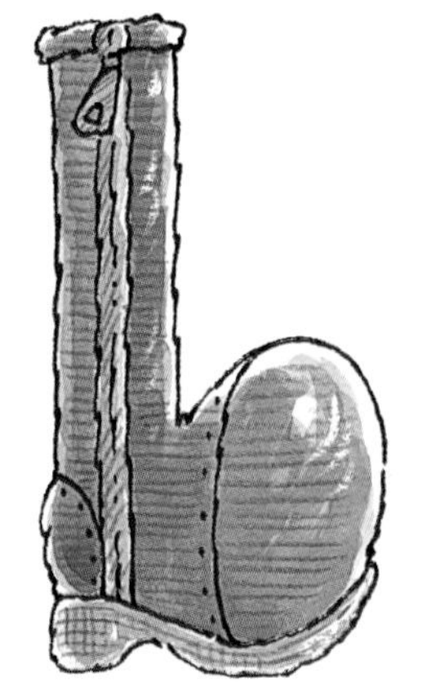

bicycle boot bag bat

ACTION

Pretend to be pulling down the long zip on the boot as you say: ***b b boot***

Encourage your child to join in, looking at the shape of her mouth in a mirror as she says the sound.

Step 3: Write the letter

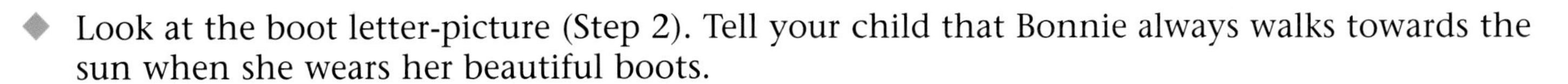

- Look at the boot letter-picture (Step 2). Tell your child that Bonnie always walks towards the sun when she wears her beautiful boots.

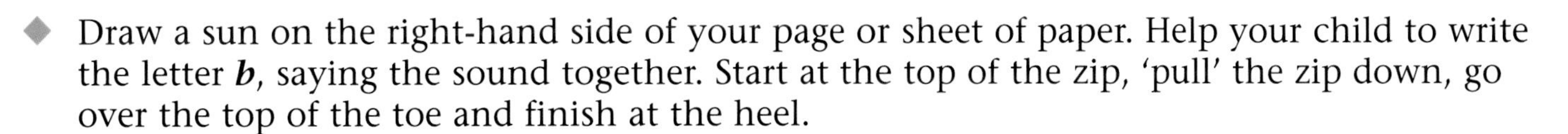

- Draw a sun on the right-hand side of your page or sheet of paper. Help your child to write the letter ***b***, saying the sound together. Start at the top of the zip, 'pull' the zip down, go over the top of the toe and finish at the heel.

Revision

HEAR THE SOUND

Look at the pictures below. Ask your child to say each word, and then to say the sound at the beginning of the word.

READ THE LETTER

Look at the letters ***b*** and ***a***, using the alphabet strip at the top of this page and page 8. Ask your child to say the sound for each one.

WRITE THE LETTER

Say the sound for ***b***, and ask your child to write the letter. Do the same with the letter ***a***. Say words that begin with each sound as she writes the letter.

Unit 3: c

a b c d e f g h i j k

Step 1: Hear the sound

- Ask your child to tell you what each of these pictures shows (*cat, caterpillar, candle, cake, cow*).
- Say each word together, repeating the first sound:

  c c cat , etc.

- Help your child to think of more things whose names begin with the sound *c* (e.g. ***carrot, coffee, cobweb, computer***).
- Help your child to think of first names which begin with the sound *c* (e.g. ***Carol, Catherine, Caspar, Calum***).

> Make the **c** sound as short as you can; try not to say ***cuh***.

> In some names beginning with ***Ch*** (e.g. ***Christopher***), the ***h*** is silent. In others (e.g. ***Chantal***), the ***Ch*** is pronounced ***Sh***. In yet other names (e.g. ***Cilla***), the ***C*** is pronounced ***S***. In this unit, concentrate on names which begin with a hard **C**, like the ones on the left.

Step 2: Read the letter

- Point to the picture of the caterpillar, saying:

  Catherine collects caterpillars crawling up cabbages.

- Say the sentence together, exaggerating the *c* sound.
- Tell your child that you can draw a picture of the sound *c*, and point to the letter *c*.
- Ask your child what he notices about the letter. (It is the same shape as the caterpillar.)
- Ask your child to point to the first letter in each of the words below and to say the sound. Read the complete word to him. Look for other letters which he has already learned.

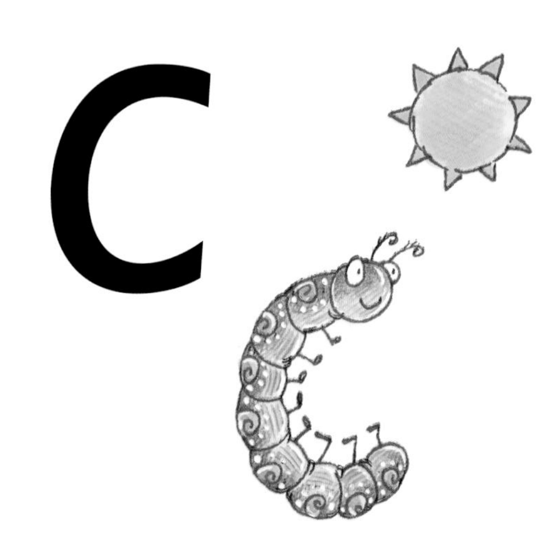

cat	caterpillar	candle	cake

ACTION

Pretend to be stroking the caterpillar's back as you say: ***c c caterpillar***

Encourage your child to join in, looking at the shape of his mouth in a mirror as he says the sound.

Step 3: Write the letter

- Look at the caterpillar letter-picture (Step 2). Tell your child that the caterpillar always faces the sun as he eats cauliflowers and cabbages.
- Draw a sun on the right-hand side of your paper. Help your child to write the letter *c*, saying the sound together. Start at the head, and curl right round the body.

> The letter ***c*** looks like the letter ***a***, but has a simpler shape because there is no downstroke.

Revision

HEAR THE SOUND

Look at the pictures below. Ask your child to say each word, and then to say the sound at the beginning of the word.

READ THE LETTER

Look at the letters *c*, ***b*** and ***a***, using the alphabet strip at the top of this page and page 10. Ask your child to say the sound for each one.

WRITE THE LETTER

Say the sounds for the letters *c*, ***b*** and ***a***, asking your child to write each letter.
Say words that begin with each sound as he writes the letter.
Do this a few times, changing the order in which you say the sounds.

Unit 4: d

a b c d e f g h i j k

Step 1: Hear the sound

- Ask your child to tell you what each of these pictures shows (***dog, dice, dinosaur, doll, duck***).

- Say each word together, repeating the first sound:

  d d dog , etc.

> Make the ***d*** sound as short as you can; try not to say ***duh***.

- Help your child to think of more things whose names begin with the sound ***d*** (e.g. ***doctor, dentist, donkey, dragon***).

- Help your child to think of first names which begin with the sound ***d*** (e.g. ***Daniel, Dominic, Danielle, Daisy***).

Step 2: Read the letter

- Point to the picture of the dinosaur, saying:

  This is a diplodocus, a long-necked dinosaur.

- Say the sentence together, exaggerating the ***d*** sound.

- Tell your child that you can draw a picture of the sound ***d***, and point to the letter ***d***.

- Ask your child what she notices about the letter. (It is the same shape as the dinosaur.)

- Ask your child to point to the first letter in each of the words below and to say the sound. Read the complete word to her. Look for other letters which she has already learned.

dog	dice	doll	dinosaur

ACTION

Stretch your arm as though it is the long neck of the dinosaur.
Make your fingers 'eat' some leaves at the top of a tree as you say: ***d d dinosaur***

Encourage your child to join in, looking at the shape of her mouth in a mirror as she says the sound.

Step 3: Write the letter

- Look at the dinosaur letter-picture (Step 2). Show your child how the dinosaur looks towards the sun.
- Draw a sun on the right-hand side of your paper. Help your child to write the letter ***d***, saying the sound together. Start at the shoulder of the dinosaur, and go over its back, under its tummy, all the way up its long neck and then all the way down to its front feet.

Revision

HEAR THE SOUND

Look at the pictures below. Ask your child to say each word, and then to say the sound at the beginning of the word.

READ THE LETTER

Look at the letters ***d***, ***c***, ***b*** and ***a***, using the alphabet strip at the top of this page and page 12. Ask your child to say the sound for each one.

WRITE THE LETTER

Say the sounds for the letters ***d***, ***c***, ***b*** and ***a***, asking your child to write each letter.
Say words that begin with each sound as she writes the letter.
Do this a few times, changing the order in which you say the sounds.

Unit 5: *e*

Step 1: Hear the sound

- Ask your child to tell you what each of these pictures shows (***elephant, egg, elbow, engine, envelope***).
- Say each word together, repeating the first sound: ***e e elephant*** , etc.
- Help your child to think of more things whose names begin with the sound ***e*** (e.g. ***elf, escape, end, emperor***).
- Help your child to think of first names which begin with the sound ***e*** (e.g. ***Edward, Ellie, Erica, Esther***).

In some names beginning with ***E*** (e.g. ***Evie***), the ***E*** is pronounced ***Ee***. In this unit, concentrate on names which begin with a short ***E***, like the ones on the left.

Step 2: Read the letter

- Point to the picture of the egg, saying:

  Eddie expects eleven eggs every day.

- Say the sentence together, exaggerating the ***e*** sound.
- Tell your child that you can draw a picture of the sound ***e***, and point to the letter ***e***.
- Ask your child what he notices about the letter. (It is the same shape as the egg.)
- Ask your child to point to the first letter in each of the words below and to say the sound. Read the complete word to him. Look for other letters which he has already learned.

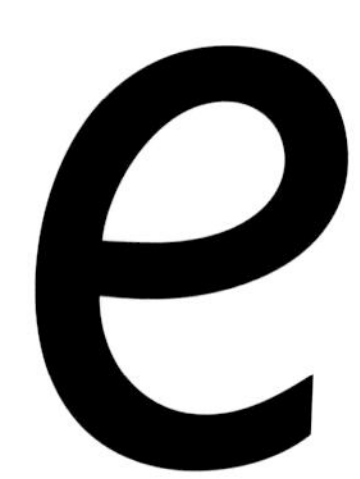

elbow	egg	elephant	engine

ACTION

Pretend to be eating a boiled egg. Let the spoon rest on your tongue as you say: ***e e egg***

Encourage your child to join in, looking at the shape of his mouth in a mirror as he says the sound.

Step 3: Write the letter

- Look at the egg letter-picture (Step 2).
- Draw a sun on the right-hand side of your paper. Help your child to write the letter ***e***, saying the sound together. 'Lift' the top off the egg, and go right round the curve of the egg and the eggcup.

Revision

HEAR THE SOUND

Look at the pictures below. Ask your child to say each word, and then to say the sound at the beginning of the word.

READ THE LETTER

Look at the letters ***e***, ***d***, ***c***, ***b*** and ***a***, using the alphabet strip at the top of this page and page 14. Ask your child to say the sound for each one.

WRITE THE LETTER

Say the sounds for the letters ***e***, ***d***, ***c***, ***b*** and ***a***, asking your child to write each letter.
Say words that begin with each sound as he writes the letter.
Do this a few times, changing the order in which you say the sounds.

Step 1: Hear the sound

- Ask your child to tell you what each of these pictures shows (***fish, fork, flower, fire engine, feather***).
- Say each word together, repeating the first sound:

  f f fish , etc.

> Make the *f* sound as short as you can; try not to say ***fuh***.

- Help your child to think of more things whose names begin with the sound *f* (e.g. ***foot, fox, frog, face***).
- Help your child to think of first names which begin with the sound *f* (e.g. ***Francesca, Floyd, Fiona, Freddie***).

Step 2: Read the letter

- Point to the picture of the flower, saying:

  Freddie and his friends like finding flowers.

- Say the sentence together, exaggerating the *f* sound.
- Tell your child that you can draw a picture of the sound *f*, and point to the letter *f*.
- Ask your child what she notices about the letter. (It is the same shape as the flower.)
- Ask your child to point to the first letter in each of the words below and to say the sound. Read the complete word to her. Look for other letters which she has already learned.

fish	flower	fire engine	feather

ACTION

'Draw' the flower in the air. Start at the flower head, go down the stalk and then draw the leaves as you say: ***ff flower***

Encourage your child to join in, looking at the shape of her mouth in a mirror as she says the sound.

Step 3: Write the letter

- Look at the flower letter-picture (Step 2). Show your child how it is turning towards the sun so that the sunlight can help it to grow.
- Draw a sun on the right-hand side of your paper. Help your child to write the letter *f*, saying the sound together. Start at the flower head, go round the curve and then straight down the stalk. Add the 'leaves' last of all, moving the pencil from left to right.

Revision

HEAR THE SOUND

Look at the pictures below. Ask your child to say each word, and then to say the sound at the beginning of the word.

READ THE LETTER

Read all the letters learned so far, using the alphabet strip at the top of this page and page 16. Ask your child to say the sound for each one.

WRITE THE LETTER

Say the sounds for some of the letters learned so far, asking your child to write each letter.
Say words that begin with each sound as she writes the letter.
Do this a few times, changing the order in which you say the sounds.

Unit 7: g

Step 1: Hear the sound

- Ask your child to tell you what each of these pictures shows (***gate, girl, guitar, goat, goose***).
- Say each word together, repeating the first sound:

  g g gate , etc.

> Make the ***g*** sound as short as you can; try not to say ***guh***.

- Help your child to think of more things whose names begin with the sound *g* (e.g. ***garage, garden, gorilla, gold***).
- Help your child to think of first names which begin with the sound *g* (e.g. ***Gaby, Gopal, Grace, Gary***).

> In some names beginning with **G** (e.g. ***George***), the **G** is pronounced ***J***. In this unit, concentrate on names which begin with a hard **G**, like the ones on the left.

Step 2: Read the letter

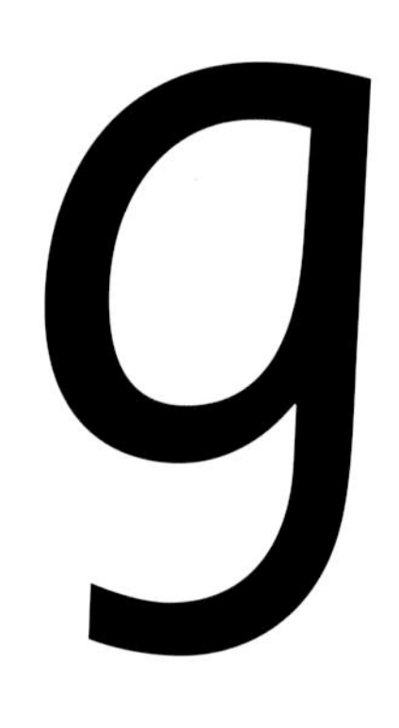

- Point to the picture of the girl, saying:

  This girl has a green ribbon.

- Say the sentence together, exaggerating the *g* sound.
- Tell your child that you can draw a picture of the sound *g*, and point to the letter *g*.
- Ask your child what he notices about the letter. (It is the same shape as the girl's head.)
- Ask your child to point to the first letter in each of the words below and to say the sound. Read the complete word to him. Look for other letters which he has already learned.

goat	gate	girl	guitar

ACTION

Pretend that you are brushing the girl's long hair as you say: ***g g girl***

Encourage your child to join in, looking at the shape of his mouth in a mirror as he says the sound.

Step 3: Write the letter

- Look at the girl letter-picture (Step 2). Show your child how she has turned away from the sun.
- Draw a sun on the right-hand side of your paper. Help your child to write the letter *g*, saying the sound together. Start at the ribbon in the girl's hair, go over the top of her head, down her face and back up to her ribbon. Then draw her plait, which curves at the bottom.

Revision

HEAR THE SOUND

Look at the pictures below. Ask your child to say each word, and then to say the sound at the beginning of the word.

READ THE LETTER

Read all the letters learned so far, using the alphabet strip at the top of this page and page 18. Ask your child to say the sound for each one.

WRITE THE LETTER

Say the sounds for some of the letters learned so far, asking your child to write each letter.
Say words that begin with each sound as he writes the letter.
Do this a few times, changing the order in which you say the sounds.

Unit 8: h

Step 1: Hear the sound

- Ask your child to tell you what each of these pictures shows (***helicopter, horse, house, hat, hedgehog***).
- Say each word together, repeating the first sound:

  h h helicopter, etc.

Make the ***h*** sound as short as you can; try not to say ***huh***.

- Help your child to think of more things whose names begin with the sound ***h*** (e.g. ***honey, hamster, hen, hedge***).
- Help your child to think of first names which begin with the sound ***h*** (e.g. ***Helen, Harry, Henry, Hannah***).

Step 2: Read the letter

- Point to the picture of the horse, saying:

  This horse belongs to Helen and Harry.

- Say the sentence together, exaggerating the ***h*** sound.
- Tell your child that you can draw a picture of the sound ***h***, and point to the letter ***h***.
- Ask your child what she notices about the letter. (It is the same shape as the horse.)
- Ask your child to point to the first letter in each of the words below and to say the sound. Read the complete word to her. Look for other letters which she has already learned.

helicopter	horse	house	hedgehog

ACTION

Pretend to take the reins of the horse as you say: ***h h horse***

Encourage your child to join in, looking at the shape of her mouth in a mirror as she says the sound.

Step 3: Write the letter

- Look at the horse letter-picture (Step 2). Show your child how the horse likes to have his back towards the sun.
- Draw a sun on the right-hand side of your paper. Help your child to write the letter ***h***, saying the sound together. Start at the horse's head, and go down his neck and his front legs. Then go over his back and down his tail.

Revision

HEAR THE SOUND

Look at the pictures below. Ask your child to say each word, and then to say the sound at the beginning of the word.

READ THE LETTER

Read all the letters learned so far, using the alphabet strip at the top of this page and page 20. Ask your child to say the sound for each one.

WRITE THE LETTER

Say the sounds for some of the letters learned so far, asking your child to write each letter.
Say words that begin with each sound as she writes the letter.
Do this a few times, changing the order in which you say the sounds.

Unit 9: i

a b c d e f g h i j k

Step 1: Hear the sound

- Ask your child to tell you what each of these pictures shows (***instruments, insect, invitation, injection, itch***).
- Say each word together, repeating the first sound:

  i i instruments , etc.

- Help your child to think of more things whose names begin with the sound ***i*** (e.g. ***illness, infant, Internet, invalid***).
- Help your child to think of first names which begin with the sound ***i*** (e.g. ***Imran, Isobel, Imogen, India***).

Step 2: Read the letter

- Point to the picture of the insect, saying:

  Inquisitive insects make Isobel itch.

- Say the sentence together, exaggerating the ***i*** sound.
- Tell your child that you can draw a picture of the sound ***i***, and point to the letter ***i***.
- Ask your child what he notices about the letter. (It is the same shape as the insect.)
- Ask your child to point to the first letter in each of the words below and to say the sound.
  Read the complete word to him.
  Look for other letters which he has already learned.

insect	injection	invitation	instruments

ACTION

Use your forefinger to 'sting' your arm as you say: ***i i insect***

Encourage your child to join in, looking at the shape of his mouth in a mirror as he says the sound.

Step 3: Write the letter

- Look at the insect letter-picture (Step 2). Show your child how the insect's tail always points towards the sun.
- Draw a sun on the right-hand side of your paper. Help your child to write the letter ***i***, saying the sound together. Start at the top of the insect's body, and go down to his curly tail. Finally, add a dot for his head.

Revision

HEAR THE SOUND

Look at the pictures below. Ask your child to say each word, and then to say the sound at the beginning of the word.

READ THE LETTER

Read all the letters learned so far, using the alphabet strip at the top of this page and page 22. Ask your child to say the sound for each one.

WRITE THE LETTER

Say the sounds for some of the letters learned so far, asking your child to write each letter.
Say words that begin with each sound as he writes the letter.
Do this a few times, changing the order in which you say the sounds.

Step 1: Hear the sound

- Ask your child to tell you what each of these pictures shows (*jam, jack-in-the-box, jug, jelly, jigsaw*).

Make the *j* sound as short as you can; try not to say *juh*.

- Say each word together, repeating the first sound: **j j jam** , etc.
- Help your child to think of more objects whose names begin with the sound ***j*** (e.g. ***jeans, jumper, jacket, jogger***).
- Help your child to think of first names which begin with the sound ***j*** (e.g. ***Jack, Julie, Jacob, Joanna***).

Step 2: Read the letter

- Point to the picture of the jack-in-the-box, saying:

  Jack jumps joyfully.

- Say the sentence together, exaggerating the ***j*** sound.
- Tell your child that you can draw a picture of the sound ***j***, and point to the letter ***j***.
- Ask your child what she notices about the letter. (It is the same shape as the jack-in-the-box.)
- Ask your child to point to the first letter in each of the words below and to say the sound. Read the complete word to her. Look for other letters which she has already learned.

jam	jack-in-the-box	jelly	jigsaw

ACTION

Pretend to be a jack-in-the-box, jumping as you say: ***j j jack-in-the-box***

Encourage your child to join in, looking at the shape of her mouth in a mirror as she says the sound.

Step 3: Write the letter

- Look at the jack-in-the-box letter-picture (Step 2). Explain that the jack-in-the-box always jumps out to face the sun because he spends most of his time in the dark.
- Draw a sun on the right-hand side of your paper. Help your child to write the letter ***j***, saying the sound together. Start at the top of Jack's body, draw down his body and then curl round his spring. Last of all, draw a dot for his head.

Revision

HEAR THE SOUND

Look at the pictures below. Ask your child to say each word, and then to say the sound at the beginning of the word.

READ THE LETTER

Read all the letters learned so far, using the alphabet strip at the top of this page and page 24. Ask your child to say the sound for each one.

WRITE THE LETTER

Say the sounds for some of the letters learned so far, asking your child to write each letter.
Say words that begin with each sound as she writes the letter.
Do this a few times, changing the order in which you say the sounds.

Step 1: Hear the sound

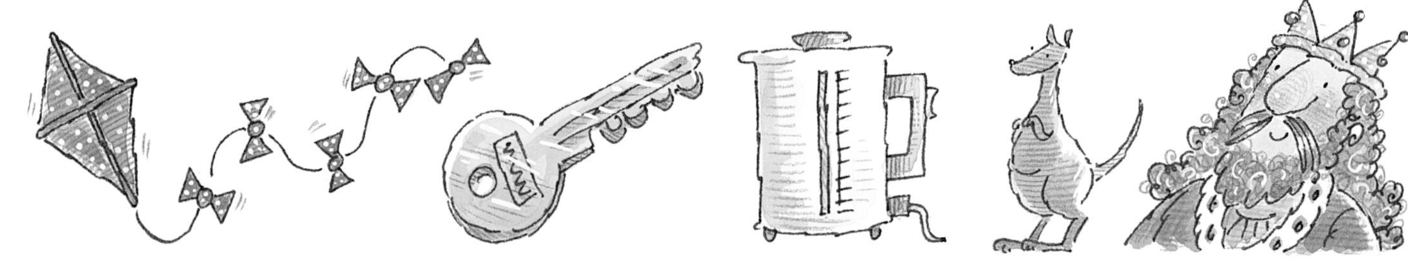

- Ask your child to tell you what each of these pictures shows (***kite, key, kettle, kangaroo, king***).
- Say each word together, repeating the first sound:

  k k kite, etc.

- Help your child to think of more things whose names begin with the sound ***k*** (e.g. ***kitten, kennel, kiss, kitchen***).
- Help your child to think of first names which begin with the sound ***k*** (e.g. ***Kelly, Karim, Kieran, Kylie***).

Make the ***k*** sound as short as you can; try not to say ***kuh***.

In some words beginning with ***k*** (e.g. ***knife***), the ***k*** is silent. Try to avoid using these in this unit.

If your child suggests names such as ***Cathy*** or ***Clive***, explain that ***C*** can make the same sound as ***K***.

Step 2: Read the letter

- Point to the picture of the kangaroo, saying:

  Kangaroos kick.

- Say the sentence together, exaggerating the ***k*** sound.
- Tell your child that you can draw a picture of the sound ***k***, and point to the letter ***k***.
- Ask your child what he notices about the letter. (It is the same shape as the kangaroo.)
- Ask your child to point to the first letter in each of the words below and to say the sound. Read the complete word to him. Look for other letters which he has already learned.

kite	key	kettle	king

ACTION

Kick your leg out as you say: ***k k kangaroo***

Encourage your child to join in, looking at the shape of his mouth in a mirror as he says the sound.

Step 3: Write the letter

- Look at the kangaroo letter-picture (Step 2). Show your child how the kangaroo turns his back to the sun when he runs away from his enemy.
- Draw a sun on the right-hand side of your paper. Help your child to write the letter ***k***, saying the sound together. Start at the kangaroo's head and go down to his right foot. Then make his tail, and then his left leg.

Revision

HEAR THE SOUND

Look at the pictures below. Ask your child to say each word, and then to say the sound at the beginning of the word.

READ THE LETTER

Read all the letters learned so far, using the alphabet strip at the top of this page and page 26. Ask your child to say the sound for each one.

WRITE THE LETTER

Say the sounds for some of the letters learned so far, asking your child to write each letter.
Say words that begin with each sound as he writes the letter.
Do this a few times, changing the order in which you say the sounds.

Step 1: Hear the sound

- Ask your child to tell you what each of these pictures shows (*leaf, ladybird, leg, lemon, ladder*).
- Say each word together, repeating the first sound:

  l l leaf , etc.

Make the *l* sound as short as you can; try not to say *luh*.

- Help your child to think of more things whose names begin with the sound ***l*** (e.g. ***lion, lamb, letter, lolly***).
- Help your child to think of first names which begin with the sound ***l*** (e.g. ***Laura, Louise, Liam, Leon***).

Step 2: Read the letter

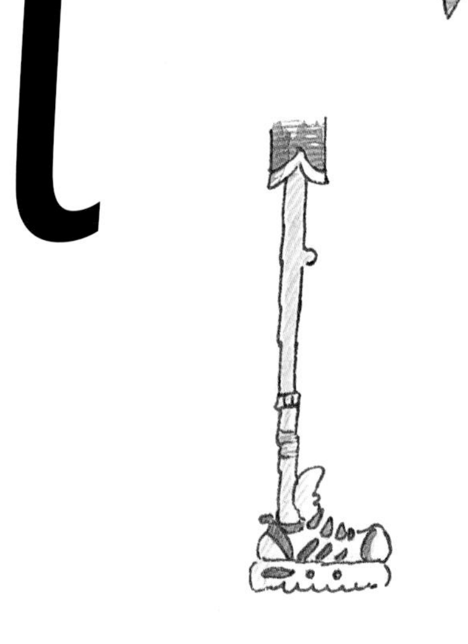

- Point to the picture of the leg, saying:

  Liam has the longest legs in the class.

- Say the sentence together, exaggerating the ***l*** sound.
- Tell your child that you can draw a picture of the sound ***l***, and point to the letter ***l***.
- Ask your child what she notices about the letter. (It is the same shape as Liam's leg.)
- Ask your child to point to the first letter in each of the words below and to say the sound.
  Read the complete word to her.
  Look for other letters which she has already learned.

ladybird	leg	lemon	ladder

ACTION

Use your first two fingers as 'legs'. Make them 'leap' as you say: ***l l legs***

Encourage your child to join in, looking at the shape of her mouth in a mirror as she says the sound.

Step 3: Write the letter

- Look at the leg letter-picture (Step 2). Show your child how Liam always faces the sun.
- Draw a sun on the right-hand side of your paper. Help your child to write the letter ***l***, saying the sound together. Start at the top of the leg, and go all the way down to the toes.

Revision

HEAR THE SOUND

Look at the pictures below. Ask your child to say each word, and then to say the sound at the beginning of the word.

READ THE LETTER

Read all the letters learned so far, using the alphabet strip at the top of this page and page 28. Ask your child to say the sound for each one.

WRITE THE LETTER

Say the sounds for some of the letters learned so far, asking your child to write each letter.
Say words that begin with each sound as she writes the letter.
Do this a few times, changing the order in which you say the sounds.

Step 1: Hear the sound

- Ask your child to tell you what each of these pictures shows (***mouse, mountains, man, milk, monkey***).
- Say each word together, repeating the first sound:

  m m mouse, etc.

Make the ***m*** sound as short as you can; try not to say ***muh***.

- Help your child to think of more things whose names begin with the sound ***m*** (e.g. ***motorbike, mother, marmalade, microwave***).
- Help your child to think of first names which begin with the sound ***m*** (e.g. ***Maria, Michael, Marlon, Molly***).

Step 2: Read the letter

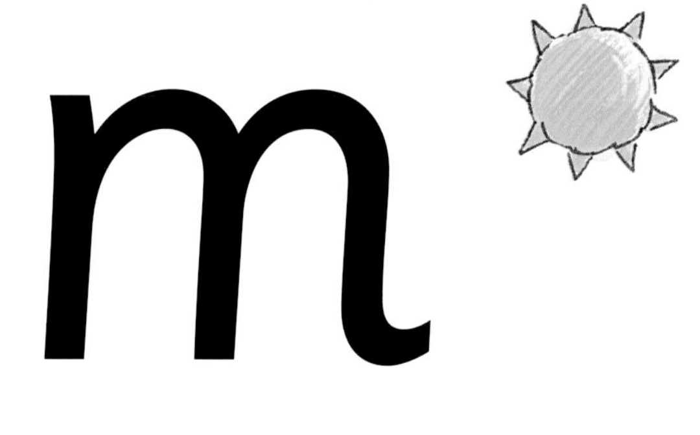

- Point to the picture of the mountains, saying:

  Maisie's marvellous mountains

- Say the phrase together, exaggerating the ***m*** sound.
- Tell your child that you can draw a picture of the sound ***m***, and point to the letter ***m***.
- Ask your child what he notices about the letter. (It is the same shape as Maisie and the mountains.)
- Ask your child to point to the first letter in each of the words below and to say the sound. Read the complete word to him. Look for other letters which he has already learned.

mouse	mountains	man	monkey

ACTION

Draw Maisie and the two mountains in the air with a finger, as you say: **m m mountains**

Encourage your child to join in, looking at the shape of his mouth in a mirror as he says the sound.

Step 3: Write the letter

- Look at the mountains letter-picture (Step 2). Show your child how Maisie is looking towards the mountains and the sun.
- Draw a sun on the right-hand side of your paper. Help your child to write the letter ***m***, saying the sound together. Start at the top of Maisie's head and go down to her feet. Then go over the two mountains.

Revision

HEAR THE SOUND

Look at the pictures below. Ask your child to say each word, and then to say the sound at the beginning of the word.

READ THE LETTER

Read all the letters learned so far, using the alphabet strip at the top of this page and page 30. Ask your child to say the sound for each one.

WRITE THE LETTER

Say the sounds for some of the letters learned so far, asking your child to write each letter.
Say words that begin with each sound as he writes the letter.
Do this a few times, changing the order in which you say the sounds.

Step 1: Hear the sound

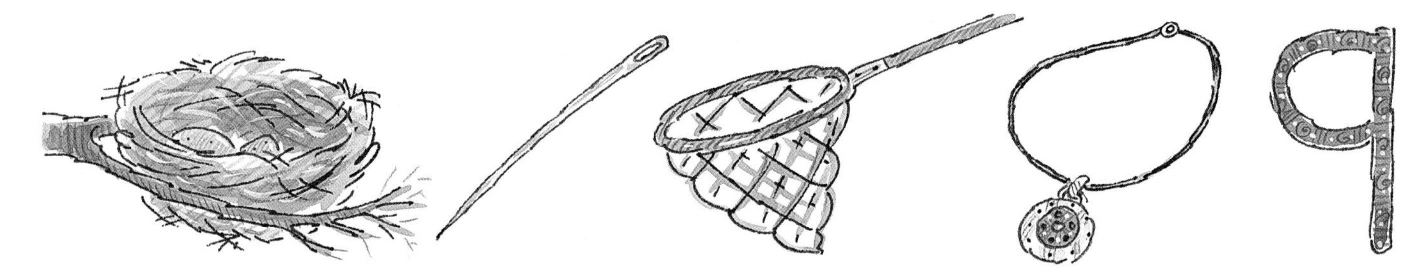

- Ask your child to tell you what each of these pictures shows (***nest, needle, net, necklace, nine***).
- Say each word together, repeating the first sound:

  n n nest , etc.

Make the ***n*** sound as short as you can; try not to say ***nuh***.

- Help your child to think of more things whose names begin with the sound ***n*** (e.g. ***nail, neck, name, nightie***).
- Help your child to think of first names which begin with the sound ***n*** (e.g. ***Nadia, Nina, Nathan, Neil***).

Step 2: Read the letter

- Point to the picture of the net, saying:

  Neil is standing next to his new net.

- Say the sentence together, exaggerating the ***n*** sound.
- Tell your child that you can draw a picture of the sound ***n***, and point to the letter ***n***.
- Ask your child what she notices about the letter. (It is the same shape as Neil and the net.)
- Ask your child to point to the first letter in each of the words below and to say the sound. Read the complete word to her. Look for other letters which she has already learned.

net	needle	necklace	nine

ACTION

Bend your two hands into an arch like Neil's net, as you say: **n n net**

Encourage your child to join in, looking at the shape of her mouth in a mirror as she says the sound.

Step 3: Write the letter

- Look at the net letter-picture (Step 2). Show your child how Neil always looks towards the sun.

- Draw a sun on the right-hand side of your paper. Help your child to write the letter ***n***, saying the sound together. Start at Neil's head and go down to his feet. Then go over the net.

Revision

HEAR THE SOUND

Look at the pictures below. Ask your child to say each word, and then to say the sound at the beginning of the word.

READ THE LETTER

Read all the letters learned so far, using the alphabet strip at the top of this page and page 32. Ask your child to say the sound for each one.

WRITE THE LETTER

Say the sounds for some of the letters learned so far, asking your child to write each letter.
Say words that begin with each sound as she writes the letter.
Do this a few times, changing the order in which you say the sounds.

Step 1: Hear the sound

- Ask your child to tell you what each of these pictures shows (***octopus, orange, ostrich, otter, olives***).
- Say each word together, repeating the first sound:

  o o octopus , etc.
- Help your child to think of more things whose names begin with the sound ***o*** (e.g. ***office, orangutan, optician, opposite***).
- Help your child to think of first names which begin with the sound ***o*** (e.g. ***Oliver, Olivia, Oscar, Otto***).

Step 2: Read the letter

- Point to the picture of the orange, saying:

  Oscar eats oranges as often as he can.
- Say the sentence together, exaggerating the ***o*** sound.
- Tell your child that you can draw a picture of the sound ***o***, and point to the letter ***o***.
- Ask your child what he notices about the letter. (It is the same shape as the orange.)
- Ask your child to point to the first letter in each of the words below and to say the sound. Read the complete word to him. Look for other letters which he has already learned.

orange	ostrich	octopus	otter

ACTION

Pucker your lips and make a circular movement round them with your finger as you say: ***o o orange***

Encourage your child to join in, looking at the shape of his mouth in a mirror as he says the sound.

Step 3: Write the letter

- Look at the orange letter-picture (Step 2). Show your child how the orange's stalk mark is facing the sun.
- Draw a sun on the right-hand side of your paper. Help your child to write the letter ***o***, saying the sound together. Start at the stalk mark, and go over the top of the orange and then all the way round.

Revision

HEAR THE SOUND

Look at the pictures below. Ask your child to say each word, and then to say the sound at the beginning of the word.

READ THE LETTER

Read all the letters learned so far, using the alphabet strip at the top of this page and page 34. Ask your child to say the sound for each one.

WRITE THE LETTER

Say the sounds for some of the letters learned so far, asking your child to write each letter. Say words that begin with each sound as he writes the letter.
Do this a few times, changing the order in which you say the sounds.

Step 1: Hear the sound

- Ask your child to tell you what each of these pictures shows (***pen, purse, pirate, parachute, pencil***).
- Say each word together, repeating the first sound:

  p p pen , etc.

Make the ***p*** sound as short as you can; try not to say ***puh***.

- Help your child to think of more things whose names begin with the sound ***p*** (e.g. ***park, paints, pasta, penguin***).
- Help your child to think of first names which begin with the sound ***p*** (e.g. ***Polly, Peter, Penny, Paul***).

Step 2: Read the letter

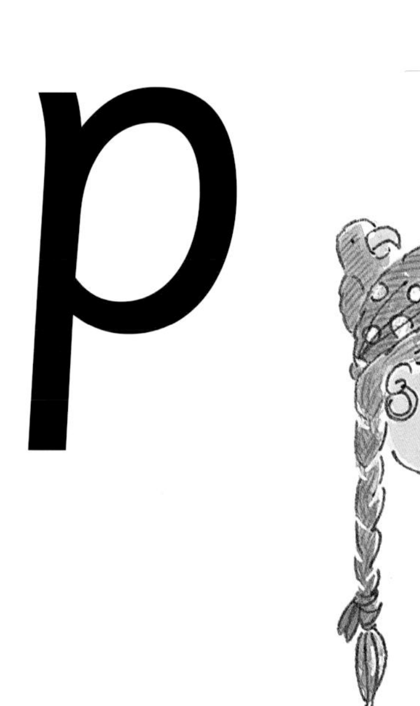

- Point to the picture of the pirate, saying:

  Polly Pirate has a purple parrot and a plait.

- Say the sentence together, exaggerating the ***p*** sound.
- Tell your child that you can draw a picture of the sound ***p***, and point to the letter ***p***.
- Ask your child what she notices about the letter. (It is the same shape as the pirate's head.)
- Ask your child to point to the first letter in each of the words below and to say the sound. Read the complete word to her. Look for other letters which she has already learned.

purse	pen	parachute	pencil

ACTION

Put your hand behind your head as you say: ***p p pirate***

Encourage your child to join in, looking at the shape of her mouth in a mirror as she says the sound.

Step 3: Write the letter

- Look at the pirate letter-picture (Step 2). Show your child how Polly always faces the sun.
- Draw a sun on the right-hand side of your paper. Help your child to write the letter ***p***, saying the sound together. Start at the top of the parrot, go down to the bottom of Polly's plait and back up again, and then go round Polly's face.

Revision

HEAR THE SOUND

Look at the pictures below. Ask your child to say each word, and then to say the sound at the beginning of the word.

READ THE LETTER

Read all the letters learned so far, using the alphabet strip at the top of this page and page 36. Ask your child to say the sound for each one.

WRITE THE LETTER

Say the sounds for some of the letters learned so far, asking your child to write each letter.
Say words that begin with each sound as she writes the letter.
Do this a few times, changing the order in which you say the sounds.

Step 1: Hear the sound

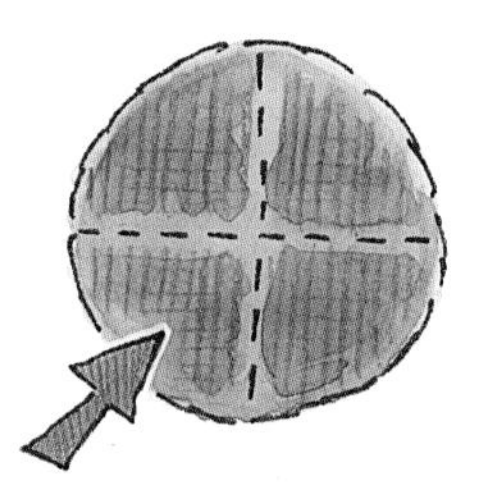

- Ask your child to tell you what each of these pictures shows (***quilt, queen, quarrel, quarter, question mark***).
- Say each word together, repeating the first sound:

  qu qu quilt , etc.

In English, the letter ***q*** is always followed by ***u***.

- Help your child to think of more things whose names begin with the sound ***q*** (e.g. ***quill, quest, quiz, quack***).
- Help your child to think of first names which begin with the sound ***q*** (e.g. ***Quentin, Queenie***).

Step 2: Read the letter

- Point to the picture of the queen, saying:

  This is a very quiet queen.

- Say the sentence together, exaggerating the ***q*** sound.
- Tell your child that you can draw a picture of the sound ***q***, and point to the letter ***q***.
- Ask your child what he notices about the letter. (It is the same shape as the queen's head.)
- Ask your child to point to the first letter in each of the words below and to say the sound. Read the complete word to him. Look for other letters which he has already learned.

queen	quilt	quarrel	question mark

ACTION

Make a crown shape on your head with your hands as you say: ***qu qu queen***

Encourage your child to join in, looking at the shape of his mouth in a mirror as he says the sound.

Step 3: Write the letter

- Look at the queen letter-picture (Step 2), and show your child how she always looks away from the sun.
- Draw a sun on the right-hand side of your paper. Help your child to write the letter ***q***, saying the sound together. Start at the back of the queen's crown, go over her head, round her face and back up to her crown. Draw her long hair with a curl at the end.

Revision

HEAR THE SOUND

Look at the pictures below. Ask your child to say each word, and then to say the sound at the beginning of the word.

READ THE LETTER

Read all the letters learned so far, using the alphabet strip at the top of this page and page 38. Ask your child to say the sound for each one.

WRITE THE LETTER

Say the sounds for some of the letters learned so far, asking your child to write each letter.
Say words that begin with each sound as he writes the letter.
Do this a few times, changing the order in which you say the sounds.

Unit 18: r

Step 1: Hear the sound

- Ask your child to tell you what each of these pictures shows (***rainbow, ring, robot, rocket, rabbit***).
- Say each word together, repeating the first sound:

  r r rainbow , etc.

> Make the *r* sound as short as you can; try not to say ***ruh***.

- Help your child to think of more things whose names begin with the sound ***r*** (e.g. ***radio, river, rose, race***).
- Help your child to think of first names which begin with the sound ***r*** (e.g. ***Richard, Ruth, Robert, Rachel***).

Step 2: Read the letter

- Point to the picture of the robot, saying:

  This robot runs very rapidly.

- Say the sentence together, exaggerating the ***r*** sound.
- Tell your child that you can draw a picture of the sound ***r***, and point to the letter ***r***.
- Ask your child what she notices about the letter. (It is the same shape as the robot.)
- Ask your child to point to the first letter in each of the words below and to say the sound. Read the complete word to her. Look for other letters which she has already learned.

rainbow	ring	rocket	rabbit

ACTION

Hold your arms out in front of you as you say: ***r r robot***

Encourage your child to join in, looking at the shape of her mouth in a mirror as she says the sound.

Step 3: Write the letter

- Look at the robot letter-picture (Step 2), and show your child how he always runs towards the sun to charge his batteries.
- Draw a sun on the right-hand side of your paper. Help your child to write the letter ***r***, saying the sound together. Start at the robot's head and go down to his feet. Then go up, and go over his arms.

Revision

HEAR THE SOUND

Look at the pictures below. Ask your child to say each word, and then to say the sound at the beginning of the word.

READ THE LETTER

Read all the letters learned so far, using the alphabet strip at the top of this page and page 40. Ask your child to say the sound for each one.

WRITE THE LETTER

Say the sounds for the letters learned so far, asking your child to write each letter.
Say words that begin with each sound as she writes the letter.
Do this a few times, changing the order in which you say the sounds.

Step 1: Hear the sound

- Ask your child to tell you what each of these pictures shows (***sock, sari, snake, seesaw, snail***).
- Say each word together, repeating the first sound: **s s sock** , etc.

> Make the ***s*** sound as short as you can; try not to say ***suh***.

- Help your child to think of more things whose names begin with the sound ***s*** (e.g. ***sandwich, sack, sauce, seed***).
- Help your child to think of first names which begin with the sound ***s*** (e.g. ***Sarah, Sadie, Simon, Sam***).

Step 2: Read the letter

- Point to the picture of the snake, saying:

  This smooth, scaly snake loves snoozing in the sun.

- Say the sentence together, exaggerating the *s* sound.
- Tell your child that you can draw a picture of the sound *s*, and point to the letter *s*.
- Ask your child what he notices about the letter. (It is the same shape as the snake.)
- Ask your child to point to the first letter in each of the words below and to say the sound. Read the complete word to him. Look for other letters which he has already learned.

snail	sock	seesaw	sari

ACTION

Pretend that your arm is a wriggling snake as you say: ***s s snake***

Encourage your child to join in, looking at the shape of his mouth in a mirror as he says the sound.

Step 3: Write the letter

- Look at the snake letter-picture (Step 2), and show your child how he always looks towards the sun. He loves the sunlight on his face.
- Draw a sun on the right-hand side of your paper. Help your child to write the letter *s*, saying the sound together. Start at the snake's head, and follow the curve of his body down to his tail.

Revision

HEAR THE SOUND

Look at the pictures below. Ask your child to say each word, and then to say the sound at the beginning of the word.

READ THE LETTER

Read all the letters learned so far, using the alphabet strip at the top of this page and page 42. Ask your child to say the sound for each one.

WRITE THE LETTER

Say the sounds for some of the letters learned so far, asking your child to write each letter.
Say words that begin with each sound as he writes the letter.
Do this a few times, changing the order in which you say the sounds.

Step 1: Hear the sound

- Ask your child to tell you what each of these pictures shows (***teddy, telephone, tree, tiger, television***).
- Say each word together, repeating the first sound:

  t t teddy , etc.

> Make the ***t*** sound as short as you can; try not to say ***tuh***.

- Help your child to think of more things whose names begin with the sound ***t*** (e.g. ***table, teeth, tadpole, tortoise***).
- Help your child to think of first names which begin with the sound ***t*** (e.g. ***Tim, Terry, Tamsin, Tina***).

Step 2: Read the letter

- Point to the picture of the tree, saying:

  This is a very tall tree.

- Say the sentence together, exaggerating the ***t*** sound.
- Tell your child that you can draw a picture of the sound ***t***, and point to the letter ***t***.
- Ask your child what she notices about the letter. (It is the same shape as the tree.)
- Ask your child to point to the first letter in each of the words below and to say the sound. Read the complete word to her. Look for other letters which she has already learned.

teddy	tree	tiger	television

ACTION

Make your arms into 'branches' as you say: ***t t tree***

Encourage your child to join in, looking at the shape of her mouth in a mirror as she says the sound.

Step 3: Write the letter

- Look at the tree letter-picture (Step 2). The long branch is nearer to the sun.
- Draw a sun on the right-hand side of your paper. Help your child to write the letter ***t***, saying the sound together. Start at the top of the tree, and go down to the bottom of the trunk and round the grass. Finally, draw the two branches in one pencil stroke, going from left to right.

Revision

HEAR THE SOUND

Look at the pictures below. Ask your child to say each word, and then to say the sound at the beginning of the word.

READ THE LETTER

Read all the letters learned so far, using the alphabet strip at the top of this page and page 44. Ask your child to say the sound for each one.

WRITE THE LETTER

Say the sounds for some of the letters learned so far, asking your child to write each letter.
Say words that begin with each sound as she writes the letter.
Do this a few times, changing the order in which you say the sounds.

Unit 21: u

Step 1: Hear the sound

- Ask your child to tell you what each of these pictures shows (*umbrella, underwear, up, upset*).

> In some words (e.g. *uniform*) and names (e.g. *Usha*) which begin with *u*, the *u* is pronounced *ew* or *oo*. Try to avoid these in this unit.

- Say each word together, repeating the first sound:

  u u umbrella , etc.

- Help your child to think of more things whose names begin with the sound *u* (e.g. *us, usher, uncle, umpire*).
- Help your child to think of first names which begin with the sound *u* (e.g. *Umberto, Uppal*).

Step 2: Read the letter

- Point to the picture of the umbrella, saying:

  This umbrella is upside-down.

- Say the sentence together, exaggerating the *u* sound.
- Tell your child that you can draw a picture of the sound *u*, and point to the letter *u*.
- Ask your child what he notices about the letter. (It is the same shape as the umbrella.)
- Ask your child to point to the first letter in each of the words below and to say the sound. Read the complete word to him. Look for other letters which he has already learned.

> Don't worry if your child points to a letter (e.g. *e* in *underwear*) which is pronounced in an unexpected way.

upset	up	underwear	umbrella

ACTION

Pretend to be holding an umbrella in the air as you say: ***u u umbrella***

Encourage your child to join in, looking at the shape of his mouth in a mirror as he says the sound.

Step 3: Write the letter

- Look at the umbrella letter-picture (Step 2), and show your child the puddle which the sun is going to dry up.
- Draw a sun on the right-hand side of your paper. Help your child to write the letter ***u***, saying the sound together. Go round the umbrella, starting on the left. Then go down to the puddle and go round it.

Revision

HEAR THE SOUND

Look at the pictures below. Ask your child to say each word, and then to say the sound at the beginning of the word.

READ THE LETTER

Read all the letters learned so far, using the alphabet strip at the top of this page and page 46. Ask your child to say the sound for each one.

WRITE THE LETTER

Say the sounds for some of the letters learned so far, asking your child to write each letter.
Say words that begin with each sound as he writes the letter.
Do this a few times, changing the order in which you say the sounds.

Step 1: Hear the sound

- Ask your child to tell you what each of these pictures shows (***vase, violin, vulture, vegetables, volcano***).
- Say each word together, repeating the first sound:

  v v vase , etc.

> Make the ***v*** sound as short as you can; try not to say ***vuh***.

- Help your child to think of more things whose names begin with the sound ***v*** (e.g. ***vest, van, video, village***).
- Help your child to think of first names which begin with the sound ***v*** (e.g. ***Vaughan, Vicky, Valerie, Vikram***).

Step 2: Read the letter

- Point to the picture of the vulture, saying:

  A vulture is a vicious bird with a very sharp beak.

- Say the sentence together, exaggerating the ***v*** sound.
- Tell your child that you can draw a picture of the sound ***v***, and point to the letter ***v***.
- Ask your child what she notices about the letter. (It is the same shape as the vulture.)
- Ask your child to point to the first letter in each of the words below and to say the sound. Read the complete word to her. Look for other letters which she has already learned.

violin	vulture	vase	vegetables

ACTION

Put your wrists together and make your hands into 'wings' as you say: ***v v vulture***

Encourage your child to join in, looking at the shape of her mouth in a mirror as she says the sound.

Step 3: Write the letter

- Look at the vulture letter-picture (Step 2).
- Draw a sun on the right-hand side of your paper. Help your child to write the letter *v*, saying the sound together. Start at the tip of the wing on the left, and go down to the vulture's head. Then go up the other wing.

Revision

HEAR THE SOUND

Look at the pictures below. Ask your child to say each word, and then to say the sound at the beginning of the word.

READ THE LETTER

Read all the letters learned so far, using the alphabet strip at the top of this page and page 48. Ask your child to say the sound for each one.

WRITE THE LETTER

Say the sounds for some of the letters learned so far, asking your child to write each letter.
Say words that begin with each sound as she writes the letter.
Do this a few times, changing the order in which you say the sounds.

Step 1: Hear the sound

- Ask your child to tell you what each of these pictures shows (***window, worm, watch, wall, web***).
- Say each word together, repeating the first sound: ***w w window*** , etc.
- Help your child to think of more things whose names begin with the sound ***w*** (e.g. ***wool, word, winter, water***).
- Help your child to think of first names which begin with the sound ***w*** (e.g. ***William, Wendy, Winston, Wayne***).

Your child may suggest words (e.g. ***wheel***) and names (e.g. ***Whitney***) which begin with ***wh***. The ***h*** is silent in most regional accents of English.

Step 2: Read the letter

- Point to the picture of the worm, saying:

This is a warm, wet, wiggly worm.

- Say the sentence together, exaggerating the ***w*** sound.
- Tell your child that you can draw a picture of the sound ***w***, and point to the letter ***w***.
- Ask your child what he notices about the letter. (It is the same shape as the worm.)
- Ask your child to point to the first letter in each of the words below and to say the sound. Read the complete word to him. Look for other letters which he has already learned.

worm	window	wall	watch

ACTION

Wiggle your forefinger as you say: ***w w worm***

Encourage your child to join in, looking at the shape of his mouth in a mirror as he says the sound.

Step 3: Write the letter

- Look at the worm letter-picture (Step 2), and show your child how he wiggles towards the sun.
- Draw a sun on the right-hand side of your paper. Help your child to write the letter ***w***, saying the sound together. Start at the end of the worm's tail, and go down, up, down and up to his head.

Revision

HEAR THE SOUND

Look at the pictures below. Ask your child to say each word, and then to say the sound at the beginning of the word.

READ THE LETTER

Read all the letters learned so far, using the alphabet strip at the top of this page and page 50. Ask your child to say the sound for each one.

WRITE THE LETTER

Say the sounds for some of the letters learned so far, asking your child to write each letter. Say words that begin with each sound as he writes the letter.
Do this a few times, changing the order in which you say the sounds.

Step 1: Hear the sound

- Ask your child to tell you what each of these pictures shows (***exit, exercise, explosion, exhaust***).
- Say each word together, repeating the first sound:

  ex ex exit, etc.

In English, if the ***x*** sound comes at the beginning of a word, an ***e*** goes in front of it to make it easier to say.

- Help your child to think of more things whose names begin with the sound ***ex*** (e.g. ***extra, expert, exhibition, excitement***).

Step 2: Read the letter

- Point to the picture of the little girl exercising, saying:

  Exana finds exercise very exciting.

- Say the sentence together, exaggerating the ***ex*** sound.
- Tell your child that you can draw a picture of the sound ***ex***, and point to the letter ***x***.
- Ask your child what she notices about the letter. (It is the same shape as Exana exercising.)
- Ask your child to point to the first two letters in each of the words below and to say the sound. Read the complete word to her. Look for other letters which she has already learned.

exit	explosion	exercise	exhaust

ACTION

Throw both arms into the air as you say: ***ex ex exercise***

Encourage your child to join in, looking at the shape of her mouth in a mirror as she says the sound.

Step 3: Write the letter

- Look at the letter-picture (Step 2).
- Draw a sun on the right-hand side of your paper. Help your child to write the letter ***x***, saying the sound together. Start at the hand on the left, and go down the leg on the right. Then lift your pencil, and go down Exana's other arm and leg.

Revision

HEAR THE SOUND

Look at the pictures below. Ask your child to say each word, and then to say the sound at the beginning of the word.

READ THE LETTER

Read all the letters learned so far, using the alphabet strip at the top of this page and page 52. Ask your child to say the sound for each one.

WRITE THE LETTER

Say the sounds for some of the letters learned so far, asking your child to write each letter.
Say words that begin with each sound as she writes the letter.
Do this a few times, changing the order in which you say the sounds.

Step 1: Hear the sound

- Ask your child to tell you what each of these pictures shows (*yolk, yak, yoghurt, yo-yo, yellow*).
- Say each word together, repeating the first sound:

  y y yolk , etc.
- Help your child to think of more things whose names begin with the sound *y* (e.g. ***yawn, yard, year, yam***).
- Help your child to think of first names which begin with the sound *y* (e.g. ***Yasmin, Yolande***).

Step 2: Read the letter

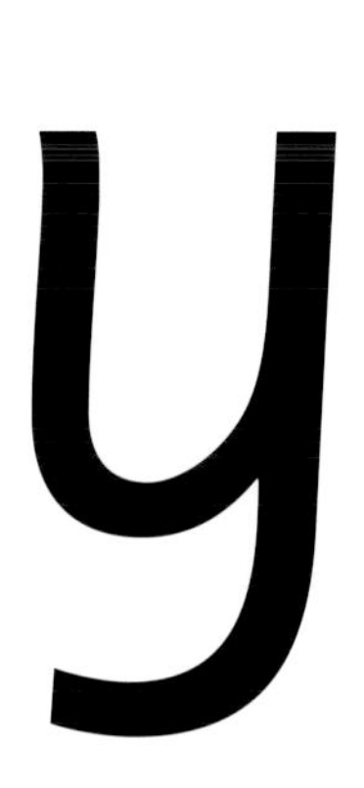

- Point to the picture of the yak, saying:

  Can you see the yellow yak?
- Say the sentence together, exaggerating the *y* sound.
- Tell your child that you can draw a picture of the sound *y*, and point to the letter *y*.
- Ask your child what he notices about the letter. (It is the same shape as the yak's head.)
- Ask your child to point to the first letter in each of the words below and to say the sound. Read the complete word to him. Look for other letters which he has already learned.

yolk	yoghurt	yo-yo	yellow

ACTION

Make 'horns' with your hands as you say: ***y y yak***

Encourage your child to join in, looking at the shape of his mouth in a mirror as he says the sound.

Step 3: Write the letter

- Look at the yak letter-picture (Step 2), and tell your child that he gets so tired in the sun that he turns his head away from it.
- Draw a sun on the right-hand side of your paper. Help your child to write the letter *y*, saying the sound together. Start at the top of the horn on the left. Go down the horn, and then go up the other horn. Then go right down the back of the yak's head and round his chin.

Revision

HEAR THE SOUND

Look at the pictures below. Ask your child to say each word, and then to say the sound at the beginning of the word.

READ THE LETTER

Read all the letters learned so far, using the alphabet strip at the top of this page and page 54. Ask your child to say the sound for each one.

WRITE THE LETTER

Say the sounds for some of the letters learned so far, asking your child to write each letter.
Say words that begin with each sound as he writes the letter.
Do this a few times, changing the order in which you say the sounds.

Unit 26: z

Step 1: Hear the sound

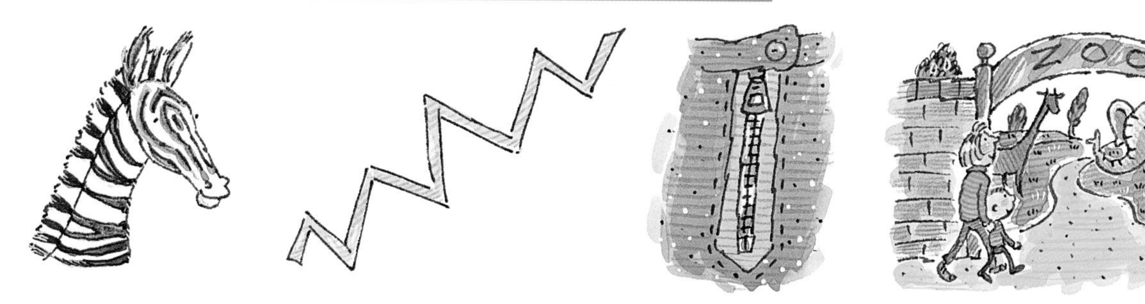

- Ask your child to tell you what each of these pictures shows (***zebra, zigzag, zip, zoo***).
- Say each word together, repeating the first sound:

  z z zebra , etc.

> Make the ***z*** sound as short as you can; try not to say ***zuh***.

- Help your child to think of more things whose names begin with the sound *z* (e.g. ***zest, zone, zodiac, zucchini, zero***).
- Help your child to think of first names which begin with the sound *z* (e.g. ***Zak, Zena, Zebedee, Zandra***).

Step 2: Read the letter

- Point to the picture of the zigzag, saying:

  Zip down the zigzagging road: zig, zag, zig, zag.

- Say the sentence together, exaggerating the *z* sound.
- Tell your child that you can draw a picture of the sound *z*, and point to the letter *z*.
- Ask your child what she notices about the letter. (It is the same shape as the zigzag.)
- Ask your child to point to the first letter in each of the words below and to say the sound. Read the complete word to her. Look for other letters.

zebra	zigzag	zip	zoo

ACTION

'Draw' the zigzag road in the air as you say: **z z zigzag**

Encourage your child to join in, looking at the shape of her mouth in a mirror as she says the sound.

Step 3: Write the letter

- Look at the letter-picture (Step 2), and show your child how the zigzag road starts by 'zigging' towards the sun.
- Draw a sun on the right-hand side of your paper. Help your child to write the letter *z*, saying the sound together. 'Zig' to the right, 'zag' to the left and 'zig' to the right again.

Revision

HEAR THE SOUND

Look at the pictures below. Ask your child to say each word, and then to say the sound at the beginning of the word.

READ THE LETTER

Read all the letters, using the alphabet strip at the top of this page and page 56. Ask your child to say the sound for each one.

WRITE THE LETTER

Say the sounds for some of the letters, asking your child to write each letter.
Say words that begin with each sound as she writes the letter.
Do this a few times, changing the order in which you say the sounds.

Step 1: Hear the sound

- Ask your child to tell you what each of these pictures shows (*chips, chocolates, chair, children, chain*).
- Say each word together, repeating the first sound:

  ch ch chips , etc.

In some words (e.g. ***chrysalis***) and names (e.g. ***Christine***) beginning with ***ch***, the ***h*** is silent. In others (e.g. ***champagne, Charlotte***) the ***ch*** is pronounced ***sh***. Try to avoid these words and names in this unit.

- Help your child to think of more things whose names begin with the sound ***ch*** (e.g. ***chicken, cheese, cherry, chilli***).
- Help your child to think of first names which begin with the sound ***ch*** (e.g. ***Chan, Charlie, Cherry, Chinta***).

Step 2: Read the letter

- Point to the picture of the caterpillar and the horse, saying: Chew, chew, chew, that's all they can do.
- Say the sentence together, exaggerating the ***ch*** sound. Tell your child that whenever he sees the caterpillar and the horse together, they make a single sound (***ch***).
- Tell your child that you can draw a picture of the sound ***ch***, and point to the letters ***ch***. Ask your child what he notices about the letters. (The ***c*** is the same shape as the caterpillar, and the ***h*** is the same shape as the horse.)

- Ask your child to point to the first two letters in each of the words below and to say the sound. Read the complete word to him. Look for other letters.

chips	chocolates	children	chair

ACTION

Make 'jaws' with your fingers and your thumb. Make a chewing movement as you say: **ch ch ch**

Encourage your child to join in, looking at the shape of his mouth in a mirror as he says the sound.

Step 3: Write the letter

- Look at the letter-picture (Step 2). Remind your child that the caterpillar faces the sun but the horse likes to have his back to it.
- Draw a sun on the right-hand side of your paper. Help your child to write the letters *c* and *h*, saying the sound together. They should be written quickly, one after the other. Make sure that your child makes the horse much taller than the caterpillar.

Revision

HEAR THE SOUND

Look at the pictures below. Ask your child to say each word, and then to say the sound at the beginning of the word.

READ THE LETTER

Read all the letters, using the alphabet strip at the top of this page and page 58. Ask your child to say the sound for each one.

WRITE THE LETTER

Say the sounds for some of the letters, asking your child to write each letter.
Say words that begin with each sound as he writes the letter.
Do this a few times, changing the order in which you say the sounds.

Step 1: Hear the sound

- Ask your child to tell you what each of these pictures shows (***shark, shell, sheep, shop, shoe***).
- Say each word together, repeating the first sound: ***sh sh shark*** , etc.
- Help your child to think of more things whose names begin with the sound ***sh*** (e.g. ***shadow, sheets, ship, show***).
- Help your child to think of first names which begin with the sound ***sh*** (e.g. ***Shaun, Shannon, Shelley, Shamina***).

Step 2: Read the letter

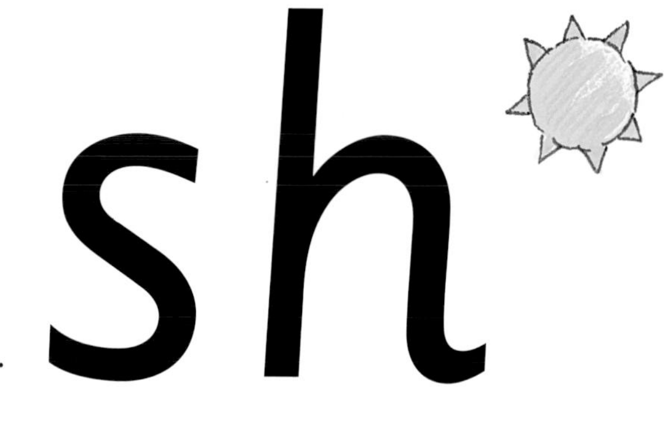

- Point to the picture of the snake and the horse, saying: The horse says to the snake, "Sh, sh, sh, give me some hush."
- Say the sentence together, exaggerating the ***sh*** sound. Tell your child that whenever she sees the snake and the horse together, they make a single sound (***sh***).
- Tell your child that you can draw a picture of the sound ***sh***, and point to the letters ***sh***. Ask your child what she notices about the letters. (The ***s*** is the same shape as the snake, and the ***h*** is the same shape as the horse.)
- Ask your child to point to the first two letters in each of the words below and to say the sound. Read the complete word to her. Look for other letters.

shark	shell	shop	shoe

ACTION

Put your finger to your lips as you say: ***sh sh sh***

Encourage your child to join in, looking at the shape of her mouth in a mirror as she says the sound.

Step 3: Write the letter

- Look at the letter-picture (Step 2). Remind your child that the snake faces the sun but the horse likes to have his back to it.
- Draw a sun on the right-hand side of your paper. Help your child to write the letters ***s*** and ***h***, saying the sound together. They should be written quickly, one after the other. Make sure that your child makes the horse much taller than the snake.

Revision

HEAR THE SOUND

Look at the pictures below. Ask your child to say each word, and then to say the sound at the beginning of the word.

READ THE LETTER

Read all the letters, using the alphabet strip at the top of this page and page 60.
Ask your child to say the sound for each one.

WRITE THE LETTER

Say the sounds for some of the letters, asking your child to write each letter.
Say words that begin with each sound as she writes the letter.
Do this a few times, changing the order in which you say the sounds.

Unit 29: th

a b c d e f g h i j k

Step 1: Hear the sound

- Ask your child to tell you what each of these pictures shows (***thumb, thief, thistle, thorn, three***).
- Say each word together, repeating the first sound: ***th th thumb***, etc.
- Help your child to think of more things whose names begin with the sound ***th*** (e.g. ***thunder, thump, throne***).
- Help your child to think of first names which begin with the sound ***th*** (e.g. ***Theo***).

> In some words beginning with ***th*** (e.g. ***this, then***), the ***th*** is 'voiced' rather than whispered. Try to avoid these words in this unit.

Step 2: Read the letter

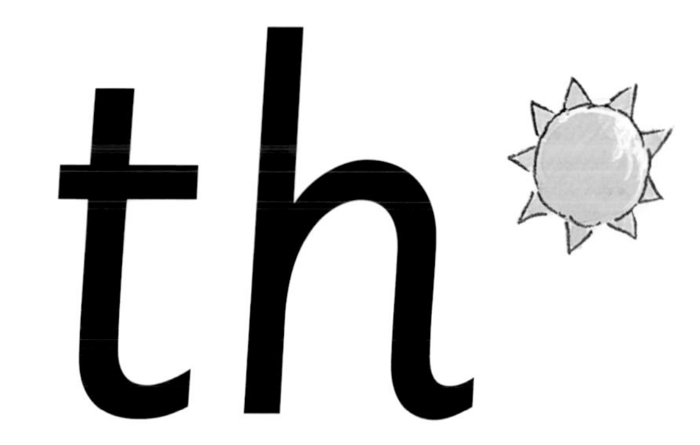

- Point to the picture of the tree and the horse, saying:

> The horse has eaten three leaves.
> He is saying thank you to the tree.

- Say the sentences together, exaggerating the ***th*** sound. Tell your child that whenever he sees the tree and the horse together, they make a single sound (***th***).
- Tell your child that you can draw a picture of the sound ***th***, and point to the letters ***th***. Ask your child what he notices about the letters. (The ***t*** is the same shape as the tree, and the ***h*** is the same shape as the horse.)
- Ask your child to point to the first two letters in each of the words below and to say the sound. Read the complete word to him. Look for other letters.

thumb	thorn	thief	three

ACTION

Pretend to be drinking a glass of water as you say: ***th th th***

Encourage your child to join in, looking at the shape of his mouth in a mirror as he says the sound.

Step 3: Write the letter

- Look at the picture of the tree and the horse (Step 2). Remind your child that the horse likes to have his back to the sun.
- Draw a sun on the right-hand side of your paper. Help your child to write the letters ***t*** and ***h***, saying the sound together. They should be written quickly, one after the other. Make sure that your child makes the horse slightly taller than the tree.

Revision

HEAR THE SOUND

Look at the pictures below. Ask your child to say each word, and then to say the sound at the beginning of the word.

READ THE LETTER

Read all the letters, using the alphabet strip at the top of this page and page 62. Ask your child to say the sound for each one.

WRITE THE LETTER

Say the sounds for some of the letters, asking your child to write each letter.
Say words that begin with each sound as he writes the letter.
Do this a few times, changing the order in which you say the sounds.

a	b	c	d	e
f	g	h	i	j
k	l	m	n	o
p	q	r	s	t
u	v	w	x	y
z	ch	sh	th	